happy

Nicola Edwards

Katie Hickey

Mindfulness

Mindfulness is all about connecting with
ourselves and the world around us.

Let's take a journey together to discover
some simple steps on the path to happiness.

Real life is right under our noses,

We can miss it by rushing around,

But stopping to smell life's sweet roses

Is where true

happiness

can be found.

Listening

When we're still

there is space then to listen

To the sweet song of wind in the trees,

The gruff rumble of cars in the distance,

Or the whisper of

rustling leaves.

Take a moment to stop and really listen to the sounds around you.

Feeling

Even the **darkest storm** passes,

The sun can't **shine bright** every day,

We can sit with our feelings and **notice**

How they **roll through us**,

then **blow away.**

What kinds of things make you feel happy?

Relaxing

It's not just our **minds** we get trapped in,

Our bodies can feel **tension** too,

We can **loosen** our limbs when that happens,

Like the **sun** from the **clouds**,

we **break through.**

Try tensing up all of your muscles

and then relaxing them, one by one.

Tasting

Whether hot, salty, sweet or sour flavour,

We taste and we chew and we feel,

If we slow when we eat, we can savour

The deliciousness of every meal.

Do you notice different textures and flavours
when you chew your food slowly?

Touching

Touch calms the **wildest emotions**,

We **connect** to the world all around,

When we dip our toes into the ocean
Or crunch crisp golden leaves on the ground.

Close your eyes and see if you can tell
what things are just by touching them.

Discovering

Exploring is one of life's pleasures,

Spot a penny, a shell or a rook,

The world's brimming with

curious treasures

For the people who

take time to look.

Look all around you

and try to spot something

you haven't noticed before.

Smelling

When we're all tangled up in our worries,

The cool air gets us grounded again,

Wood-smoke through the sharp tang of pine trees,

Or the freshness of earth after rain.

Do the things you can smell make you feel anything or bring back any memories?

Loving

The **warmth** of a hug can work **wonders**,

Being **happy** is something you feed,

With a **smile** or a **touch** or a **kindness**,

Even the tallest tree grows from a **seed**.

Have you given someone a
smile or a hug today?

Appreciating

It feels good to give thanks at the day's end

For the pink blushing sky overhead,

A hot meal, comfy shoes or a good friend,

And the warmth of a soft cosy bed.

What good things have happened in your world today?

Breathing

We **breathe deep** and expand like the galaxy,

We breathe out many **thousands of stars,**

And if ever we start to **feel** panicky,

This **reminds** us of just who we are.

Take a deep breath, hold it for two seconds

and then breathe out very slowly.

Happiness

Real life is right under our noses,

It's what's here, not the **future** or **past**,

Every day is a fresh new adventure,

Now we live in the moment, at last.

How can you be more mindful each and every day?

little senses

Nope.
Never.
Not for Me!

by Samantha Cotterill

Dial Books for Young Readers

For Gerrit

Dial Books for Young Readers
An imprint of Penguin Random House LLC, New York

Text and illustrations copyright © 2019 by Samantha Cotterill

Visit us online at Penguinrandomhouse.com

ISBN 9780525553441

Printed in China
1 3 5 7 9 10 8 6 4 2

Design by Mina Chung • Text set in Futura and Cooper Std
This art was created with ink with some pencil on watercolor paper.

Nope.
Never.
Not for me.

Just have a look,
and see what you think.

Looks bumpy . . .

too lumpy . . .

and *very* jumpy.

Nope.
Never.
Not for me!

Have a touch instead.
How does it feel?

It feels pokey!

And scratchy!

and
toooooooooo
ouchy!

Oh well, then . . .
Not every dinosaur
likes trees.

She wants to
try it first.

I think she likes it.
Perhaps you can
try it too?

Start with a sniff . . .

**then follow
with a touch . . .**

**and now
for one teeny,
little bite . . .**

gulp!

MMF!

yacky!

ROARRR!

I don't like it.

I'm not the dino I thought I was.

**Of course you are.
You're a brave "Try"ceratops
that tried something new.**

**I'm so proud
of you!**

IT!

Maybe I can try more?

I'm a "try"ceratops!

Nope.
Maybe.
Yep!
This one's for me!

I'm a
spinachia-
swissa-apple-asparaga-
triceratops...

**and apparently my
brother is a T. rex.**